Jesus Our Guide

Activity Book

Jesus Our Guide
Activity Book

Faith and Life Series

Third Edition

BOOK FOUR

Ignatius Press, San Francisco
Catholics United for the Faith, Steubenville, Ohio

Director of First Edition: The late Rev. Msgr. Eugene Kevane, Ph.D.
Assistant Director and General Editor of First Edition: Patricia Puccetti Donahoe, M.A.
First Edition Writer: Barbara M. Nacelewicz
First Edition Artist: Gary Hoff; David Previtali

Revision Writer: Colette Ellis, M.A.
Revision Editor: Caroline Avakoff, M.A.
Revision Artist: Christopher J. Pelicano

Catholics United for the Faith, Inc. and Ignatius Press gratefully acknowledge the guidance and assistance of the late Reverend Monsignor Eugene Kevane, former Director of the Pontifical Catechetical Institute, Diocese of Arlington, Virginia, in the production of the First Edition of this series. This First Edition intended to implement the authentic approach in Catholic catechesis given to the Church through documents of the Holy See and in particular the Conference of Joseph Cardinal Ratzinger on "Sources and Transmission of Faith." The Revised Edition and Third Edition continue this commitment by drawing upon the *Catechism of the Catholic Church* (Libreria Editrice Vaticana, © 1994, 1997).

Contents

Dear Student,

As you learn the Faith during this school year, you will be reading from the *Faith and Life* student text, which focuses on salvation history and God's plan for man. You will learn about how to follow Jesus and about the gifts he gives us through the Church to help us on the way to heaven. Your teacher will be helping you to understand all that you have read.

This activity book is an opportunity for you to reflect on what you have learned each week. You will find activities such as games, coloring, writing, and memorization tasks. As you work on these in class or at home, you are encouraged to think about what you read and discussed in class. Take the time to pray before and after the activities, and be sure to ask your teacher or your parents any questions that you might have.

It is our sincere hope that these activities, combined with the readings from each week, will help you to come to know Jesus Christ, and to live your life with Him.

Name:_____

Abel's Sacrifice

God was pleased with Abel's sacrifice because he offered his best, which showed that he had love in his heart. God was not pleased, however, with Cain's sacrifice because he had held back his best from God.

1. What did Abel sacrifice?

2. What did Cain sacrifice?

3. Why was God pleased with Abel's sacrifice and not Cain's?

Name:_____

Cain Kills Abel

"Let us go out into the fields," he said to his brother. Abel loved his brother very much and he did not suspect him. As soon as they were far away from everyone, Cain killed Abel. He left him there dead and alone.

Answer the following questions using complete sentences.

1. Cain thought no one else had seen his actions, but someone did know. Who else had seen what he did?

2. What did God say to Cain about the murder?

3. Was Cain sorry for his crime? Did Cain accept his punishment?

4. How did God make sure that no one would harm Cain?

Name:_____

Punishment for Sin

Answer the following questions using complete sentences.

1. How is Cain like Adam and Eve?

2. What punishments were Adam, Eve, and Cain given?

3. Why was the land cursed?

4. Did God still love the sinners?

Name:_____

Family Tree

Draw a tree around this Family Tree.

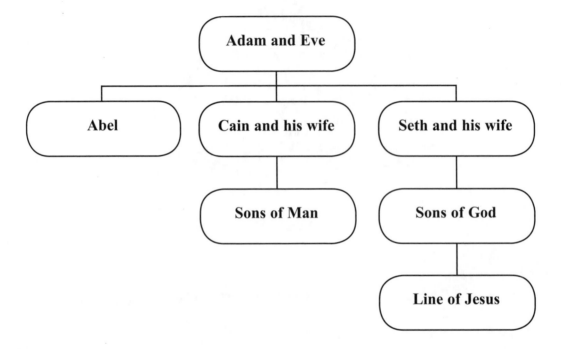

Name:_____

Come Forth Out of the Ark

Answer the following questions in complete sentences.

1. When Noah and his family left the ark, what did they do?

2. Was God pleased with their sacrifice?

3. What did God command Noah and his family to do?

4. What is the sign of God's agreement never to destroy the earth by a flood again?

5. What happened to Noah's children Shem, Japheth, and Ham?

6. What happened at Shinar?

Name:_____

Turning Away from God

Fill in the blanks in questions 1–5 to complete the word train below.

Hint: The last letter of each word is the first letter in the word that follows it. Use your student text if you need help.

1. ___ ___ ___ ___ ___ ___ ___

2. ___ ___ ___ ___ ___ ___

3. ___ ___ ___ ___

4 ___ ___ ___ ___

5. ___ ___ ___

1. God put a _____ in the sky as a sign of his promise never again to send a great flood to destroy the earth.

2. When the dove came back with an olive branch in its beak, Noah knew that the _____ was nearly gone from the earth.

3. God made it _____ for forty days and forty nights.

4. God told _____ to build an ark.

5. Noah's son, _____, had a son named Canaan.

Name:_____

Abram

Answer the following questions in complete sentences.

1. From whose descendants did Abram come?

2. What did God call Abram to do?

3. What was God asking of Abram?

4. What did Abram, Sarai, and Lot do?

5. Was Abram obedient to God? In what ways?

6. Where did Abram, Sarai, and Lot settle? Was it beautiful?

7. What did God promise Abram?

Name:_____

God's Gift: Free Will

Answer the following questions in complete sentences.

1. What did God tell Abram that he would make with him and his descendants?

2. What was the condition of this covenant?

3. What was the promise of this covenant?

4. Why did God change Abram's name? What did he change it to?

5. Why did God change Sarai's name? What did he change it to?

6. What is a covenant?

7. What would God do as his part of the covenant?

8. What would Abraham and his descendants do as their part of the covenant?

9. For what was God preparing them?

10. God fulfilled his promise to Abram and Sarai and gave Abraham and Sarah a son. What is his name?

A Test for Abraham

Answer the following questions in complete sentences.

1. What did God ask Abraham to do as a test?

2. What did Abraham do as a response?

3. When Isaac asked where the lamb for the sacrifice was, what was Abraham's reply?

4. What stopped Abraham from sacrificing Isaac?

5. What did Abraham sacrifice instead?

Name:_____

God Prepares His People for the Savior

Use your student text to solve this crossword puzzle.

Across

1. What God told Abraham to do with Isaac.

3. Abraham and Sarah's only son.

6. Abraham was a descendant of _____.

8. God told Abraham his descendants would be as many as the _____ in the sky.

9. Abraham's name before God changed it.

Down

1. Abraham's wife's new name.

2. We call Abraham our father in _____.

4. The name of the land that God promised to the descendants of Abraham.

5. God said "Walk before me and be blameless and I will make my _____ between me and you and your descendants forever."

7. God sent Abraham to the mountains in _____ to sacrifice his son.

8. Melchizedek was King of _____.

9. The name of Abraham's nephew.

Faith and Life Series • Grade 4 • Chapter 4 • Lesson 4

Name:_____

Isaac Marries Rebekah

Answer the following questions in complete sentences.

1. How did Abraham find a wife for his son Isaac?

2. Why did Abraham send his servant to the country of his birth to find a wife?

3. Did God grant children to Isaac?

4. How many children did Rebekah have?

5. Describe Esau.

Name:_____

The Birthright

Answer the following questions in complete sentences.

1. Who was the eldest son of Isaac?

2. What privilege did the eldest son usually have after the father died?

3. What is this called?

4. What had the Lord told Rebekah about this?

5. Did Esau keep his birthright?

6. For what did he sell his birthright?

7. Who now had the birthright?

8. How did this fulfill what the Lord had told Rebekah?

9. Esau swore before God. Is this serious? Must Esau keep this oath?

10. When Esau sold his birthright, what did this show?

Name:_____

Isaac Blesses Jacob

In your own words, describe how Jacob tricked Isaac into giving his blessing.

Name:_____

Trickery!

Things to think about.

Jacob had tricked Esau for his birthright and his father Isaac for Esau's blessing! Jacob was dishonest, but God knew how to bring good out of evil. Through all this trickery, the word of the Lord to Rebekah had been fulfilled.

Esau, however, became very angry with Jacob and wanted to kill him. Rebekah loved her son Jacob and sent him to live with his uncle Laban. Laban had two daughters and Jacob fell in love with Rachel. He arranged to marry her in exchange for seven years of work.

Laban wanted his other daughter Leah to be married first because she was older, so Laban tricked Jacob into marrying Leah. Jacob then married Rachel, but he had to work another seven years.

Jacob had many children. In fact, he had twelve boys. These twelve boys would become the twelve tribes of Israel, for Jacob's name was changed to Israel. The twelve sons' names were: Reuben, Simeon, Levi, Judah (Jesus would come from Judah's line), Dan, Naphtali, Gad, Asher, Issachar, Zebulun, Joseph, and Benjamin.

Name:_____

Joseph

Answer the following questions in complete sentences.

1. Why were Joseph's brothers envious of him?

2. What did Joseph dream the first time?

3. What did Joseph dream the second time?

4. Why did Israel send Joseph out to his brothers?

5. What did his brothers plan to do to him?

6. What did Reuben tell them to do? Why?

Name:_____

Joseph Sold into Slavery

Answer the following questions using complete sentences.

1. What did Joseph's brothers do to get rid of him?

2. Why didn't they kill him?

3. What did they do to his coat?

4. Whom did they sell Joseph to?

5. Where did Joseph end up?

6. What was Joseph's assignment when he arrived in Egypt?

Name:_____

Joseph Interprets Pharaoh's Dreams

Answer the following questions in complete sentences.

1. What did Pharaoh dream?

2. How did Pharaoh learn of Joseph's gift to read dreams?

3. What did Joseph tell Pharaoh his dreams meant?

4. What did Joseph suggest Pharaoh should do?

5. How did Pharaoh reward Joseph?

Prayer For Enduring Hardships

Joseph endured many hardships in his life, but God made many of them become great graces.

Write a prayer asking God to do the same for you. Or, you may write a prayer that you think Joseph would have prayed to God in time of trial.

Dear God,

_____

_____

_____

_____

_____

_____

_____

_____

_____

_____

_____

_____

_____

Name:_____

Joseph Tests His Brothers

Things to think about.

The Land of Canaan was also suffering from the famine. When Israel heard about the food in Egypt, he sent his sons to buy some, but he kept little Benjamin with him because he was afraid that he would lose him as he had lost Joseph.

In Egypt, Joseph recognized his brothers, but treated them like strangers to see if they were sorry for treating him so badly. He accused them of being spies. He kept Simeon in prison until they would return with Benjamin. This was their test to see if they were repentant, and a chance for Joseph to see his younger brother again.

If the Sons of Israel wanted to release their brother Simeon from jail and buy more grain, they would have to return with Benjamin and this would be difficult because old Israel loved him so.

Joseph's Dreams Had Come True

Name:_____

Benjamin

Answer the following questions in complete sentences.

1. What did Joseph do when he saw his brother Benjamin?

2. Why did Joseph put his cup in Benjamin's bag?

3. What did Judah say to save Benjamin?

4. When did Joseph reveal his secret?

5. Was it part of God's plan that Joseph was taken to Egypt? Why or why not?

Name:_____

In Egypt

Answer the following questions in complete sentences.

1. Did Israel want to go to Egypt?

2. How did he know it was okay to go?

3. What did God tell Israel would happen to his descendants?

4. What happened when Israel and Joseph were reunited?

5. When did Israel die and where was he buried?

Name:_____

Slavery

Answer the following questions in complete sentences.

1. Why did Pharaoh make the Israelites slaves?

2. How did Pharaoh plan to control the Israelites?

3. What happened to the newborn sons of the Israelites?

4. What did the Israelites try to do to their newborn sons?

Name:_____

Moses

Answer the following questions.

1. Why did Moses' mother and sister put him in a basket and send him down the Nile?

2. Who found Moses?

3. Who took care of him?

4. Who adopted him?

Name:_____

God's People Suffer in Egypt

Use your book to help you find the answers hidden in the pyramid. Hint: The words can be spelled in any direction.

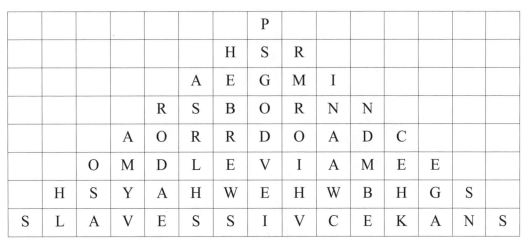

						P					
					H	S	R				
				A	E	G	M	I			
			R	S	B	O	R	N	N		
		A	O	R	R	D	O	A	D	C	
	O	M	D	L	E	V	I	A	M	E	E
	H	S	Y	A	H	W	E	H	W	B	H	G	S
S	L	A	V	E	S	S	I	V	C	E	K	A	N	S

1. Pharaoh decided to make the Hebrews _____.

2. Who decided to put all the Hebrew baby boys to death?

3. Who were the people who suffered in Egypt?

4. One day a little boy was _____ into the tribe of _____.

5. The little boy's name was _____.

6. The daughter of Pharaoh was a _____.

7. Who talked to Moses from the burning bush?

8. What did God tell Moses his name is? What is the Hebrew word meaning "I Am?"

Name:_____

The Burning Bush

1. When Moses saw the burning bush, what was he instructed to do? Why?

2. How did God identify himself? Whose God is he?

3. What mission did God have for Moses?

4. What is God's name?

5. What did God give to Moses so that people would believe him?

6. Who would speak for Moses?

7. Did people believe him?

Name:_____

God provides

God provided for the needs of the Israelites when they were on their way to the Promised Land. He gave them manna and quail to eat! God takes care of you too!

Think of some of the many ways God takes care of you and write a letter to God thanking him.

Dear God,

_____

_____

_____

_____

_____

_____

_____

_____

_____

_____

_____

_____

_____

_____

_____

_____

_____

_____

_____

The Golden Calf

Answer the following questions in complete sentences.

1. Why did the Israelites make the golden calf?

2. Where was Moses at the time?

3. Who made the calf and from what?

4. What is an idol (see the glossary in your student text), and how did the Israelites commit the sin of idolatry?

5. What did Moses do?

Name:_____

The Covenant with Israel

Answer the following questions in complete sentences.

1. God made a covenant with the people of Israel at Mount Sinai. He said to them: "If you will obey my voice and keep my covenant, you shall be my own possession. You shall be a Kingdom of priests and a consecrated nation." What did the Israelites reply to this?

2. Describe what the Israelites saw on the mountain while Moses talked with God.

3. How long was Moses on the mountain?

4. What did God give to Moses?

5. When Moses came down the mountain, the Israelites were sinning greatly by worshipping the golden calf. Moses was so upset that he threw down the Ten Commandments and shattered them. Moses had to go back up the mountain to renew the covenant with God. For how long did he go up?

6. Where was Moses to take God's chosen people?

7. Why did God give the people his laws?

8. When Moses came down the mountain, what did he look like?

Name: _____

Way to the Promised Land

Unscramble the words in parentheses to complete the sentences below. Use your book if you need help.

1. When the people of Israel ran out of the (odfo) __food__ , God sent a heavy dew to cover the ground.

2. When the dew evaporated, it left behind white, flaky (drabe) __bread__ , which tasted of honey.

3. They called it (nmnaa) __manna__ .

4. God provided fresh manna each (groimnn) __morning__ for the rest of the time the Hebrews were in the desert.

Number the sentences in the order in which the events they describe happened.

__4__ The people had a feast to honor the golden calf.

__1__ Moses went up Mount Sinai to spend forty days and forty nights speaking with the Lord.

__5__ Moses came down from the mountain, threw down the tablets with the Commandments, and punished the people for their sin.

__2__ God gave Moses the Ten Commandments carved on stone tablets.

__3__ The people of Israel grew tired of waiting for Moses, and so they gave their gold jewelry to Aaron who made a golden calf out of it

Name:_____

The Battle of Jericho

Answer the following questions in complete sentences.

1. Who took Moses' place as the leader of the Israelites?

2. How did Moses pass on God's wisdom?

3. How did the Israelites win the Battle of Jericho?

Name:_____

Samson

Answer the following questions in complete sentences.

1. Who is Samson?

2. Who was afraid of Samson?

3. What was Samson forbidden to do in order to keep his strength?

4. What did Samson use to strike down one thousand Philistines in one day?

5. Whom did Samson fall in love with?

6. Who betrayed Samson? How?

7. How did God use Samson to kill many more Philistines?

Name:_____

The Strongest Man Alive!

Use this page to write a newspaper article about Samson.

Name:_____

Naomi and Ruth

Answer the following questions in complete sentences.

1. How were Naomi and Ruth related?

2. Why did they return to Bethlehem?

3. Why didn't Orpah join them?

4. Why did Ruth stay with Naomi?

5. What happened when they were hungry? Into whose fields did Ruth go?

6. Whom did Ruth end up marrying?

7. Who became her great grandson?

Name:_____

Speak Lord, Thy Servant is Listening

Use your student text to find the words to fill in the blanks.

One night, when Samuel was sleeping near the _____, he heard
someone call, "Samuel! Samuel!" Thinking that _____ called, he
ran to his bed.

"_____ _____ _____," he said.

"I did not call you, my _____. Go back and lie down," said Eli.

Samuel lay down and heard his _____ called and ran to Eli again.
Once more _____ sent him back to bed. The _____
time when he came running to Eli, Eli guessed that it was _____
who called Samuel. "Go and lie down," he said, "and when the voice calls you,
say "_____
_____."

So Samuel lay down and the voice called him again. It was God, and Yahweh
had a mission for Samuel. What was that mission?

Name:_____

The Ark of God

Draw a picture of the Ark of God in the temple of Dagon. The statue of Dagon was found lying face down on the ground!

Name:_____

Israel's King

Answer the following questions in complete sentences.

1. Why did Israel want a king?

2. What did God say about Israel's request?

3. What did Samuel warn them with regard to having a king?

4. How was a king chosen for Israel?

5. Who was the first king? From what tribe did he come?

Name:_____

Israel Wants a King

Answer the following questions in complete sentences.

1. Was Saul a good king at first? Why?

2. Why did God remove the Kingdom from Saul?

3. What is Samuel's role? How was he God's helper?

Name: _____

David, the Shepherd Boy

Things to think about.

David was a shepherd, a priest-king, and a sign of Jesus Christ who was also a shepherd and a priest-king. David was the youngest of Jesse's sons and was chosen by God to be the second king of Israel.

David had a special talent for writing and playing music. David would play for King Saul during his time of madness. David was a good servant of Saul and he was also much loved.

Name:_____

David and Goliath

Things to think about.

You fight me armed with a sword, spear, and javelin. But I fight you in the name of the Lord of Hosts, the God of the armies of Israel, whom you have defied. Today, this God will help me defeat you. I will cut off your head so that all the earth will know that there is a God in Israel, and that it is not by the sword that God gives the victory, for it is God who is Lord of the battle.

David in Hiding

Answer the following questions in complete sentences.

1. Why did David go into hiding?

2. David could have killed King Saul. Why didn't he?

3. Where did David go to live after he had spared Saul's life?

4. How did King Saul die?

5. When David became king, what city did he attack and call the City of David?

Name:_____

Ark of the Covenant

Explain how the Ark of the Covenant came into the City of David.

Name:_____

King Solomon

Things to think about.

"Oh, my Lord!" Solomon said, "I do not know how to be king. Please give me, your servant, wisdom so that I can rule over your people. And help me to know good from evil." God was pleased that Solomon asked for these gifts. Instead of asking God for a long life and riches, he asked God for great wisdom. God rewarded Solomon and gave him great wisdom. In addition, God gave him what he had not asked for: a long life and riches!

Name:_____

The Temple of Solomon

True or false questions.

1. _____ David ordered that a Temple be built in the City of David.
2. _____ The Ark of the Covenant would be kept in the Temple where God would be worshipped.
3. _____ The Temple was made of marble.
4. _____ The Ark of the Covenant contained the laws of God.
5. _____ The entire Temple was covered with gold.
6. _____ It took several years to build the Temple.
7. _____ The high priest blessed the people when the Ark was brought in.
8. _____ The people celebrated for seven days.

Name:_____

Solomon

Answer the following questions in complete sentences.

1. For what was Solomon known?

2. What gifts would people offer Solomon in thanksgiving for his good advice?

3. What did Solomon have built?

4. How did Solomon's kingdom grow?

5. What did Solomon do that displeased God?

6. How did his wives turn his heart away from God?

7. Was Solomon a good king? Why or why not?

Name:_____

Isaiah

Answer the following questions in complete sentences.

1. Who is Isaiah?

2. What was Isaiah doing in the Temple?

3. What did Isaiah see?

4. How was Isaiah prepared to speak to God's people for God himself?

5. About what did Isaiah talk?

6. For whom did Isaiah prepare the Israelites?

7. What did Isaiah predict about the Messiah?

8. Was this what people expected from the new king?

Exile

After Solomon's death, the kingdom was divided into two: Judah and Israel. These two kingdoms soon began to fight with each other and with other kingdoms too. God sent prophets to bring his people back to him but this often failed. Soon Jerusalem was lost in a war. All the Jews had to leave and this was called the "exile." The Jews lived in exile for a very long time, but eventually they came back to Jerusalem. Once they had returned to Jerusalem, they started to await the new king that the prophets had promised.

Circle the best answer.

1. The Israelites were taken to Babylon in what we call:
   a. an exodus
   b. an exile
   c. the Temple
   d. the City of David

2. During this time, God prepared them for the coming of:
   a. a Savior
   b. a Messiah
   c. a king
   d. all of the above

3. The Messiah would be of the line of:
   a. David
   b. Moses
   c. Isaiah
   d. Levi

4. John the Baptist prepared the people for the new king by:
   a. baptism
   b. telling them to be sorry for their sins
   c. telling the people to turn back to God
   d. all of the above

Name:_____

A Newborn King!

Things to think about.

God was saddened when Israel wanted a king other than himself. Israel was now expecting a new king. Through a miracle called the Incarnation, God became man in the Divine Person of Jesus. Jesus (the Son of God) would be the new king!

God knew that Israel had much to learn. They expected a soldier, a king with wealth, a kingdom, and power here on earth. God, however, wanted what was best for his people—all of them. He wanted his Kingdom to be for everybody. He wanted his people to be united with him forever in the Kingdom of Heaven.

Jesus came as a baby born in a stable. He was weak and poor in the eyes of the world, but he really had great riches and power. He had union with God and all the riches of heaven. Jesus came to undo all that the sin of Adam and Eve had done. He came to bring life, grace, unity with God, unity with each other, and lots of love.

Name:_____

Jesus' Baptism

"This is my beloved Son, in whom I am well pleased."

Answer the following questions in complete sentences.

1. What tribe was Jesus from?

2. What happened when Jesus was baptized?

3. Why did God do this?

4. What was Jesus' work that he was now ready to begin?

Name:_____

The King

world ✓   peace ✓   stable ✓   poor ✓   fishermen ✓

Fill in the blanks with the words above.

1. The Israelites expected a king who would be rich, but Jesus was
   _____poor_____.

2. The Israelites expected a king who would live in a palace, but Jesus was born
   in a _____stable_____.

3. The Israelites wanted a king who would lead a battle against their enemies,
   but Jesus brought _____peace_____.

4. The Israelites thought that kings could only be friends with other kings and
   noble men. Jesus' friends were _____fisherman_____ and ordinary people like
   you.

5. The Israelites thought that the king would make a kingdom on the earth, but
   Jesus said his kingdom does not belong to this _____world_____.

Name:_____

Baptism

Baptism is the day you became a member of the Kingdom!

Answer the following questions in complete sentences.

1. When were you baptized?

2. Why did Jesus want you to become a Catholic Christian?

3. What did you receive at your Baptism?

4. Now that you have been baptized and are Catholic, is God still inviting you?

5. Does God force you to accept this invitation?

Name:_____

God Made Us Special!

Mark if these things can be done by:	Animals	People
1. Can *make up your mind* to do something	___	✓
2. Can *learn* religion.	___	✓
3. Can *laugh* at jokes.	___	✓
4. Can *pray*.	___	✓
5. Can *love*.	✓	✓
6. Can *study*.	___	✓
7. Can *cry when sad*.	___	✓
8. Can *give things up* as a sacrifice.	___	✓
9. Can *understand* the laws.	___	✓
10. Can *choose* to follow Jesus.	___	✓
11. Can *choose* to disobey.	___	✓
12. Can *go to heaven*.	✓	✓
13. Can *sin*.	✓	✓
14. Can *read*.	___	✓
15. Can *worship*.	___	✓

Name:_____

The Ten Commandments

Write out the Ten Commandments.

1.

2.

3.

4.

5.

6.

7.

8.

9.

10.

Answer the following questions in complete sentences.

1. Why did God give us the Ten Commandments?

2. What are the Ten Commandments our yes to?

3. Where did we get the Ten Commandments?

4. What did the Jews build to hold the Ten Commandments?

Name:_____

Jesus and the Commandments

Answer the following questions in complete sentences.

1. Did Jesus learn and keep the Ten Commandments?

2. Is it possible to follow the exact words of the Commandments but have your heart far from God?

3. Why did Jesus teach the people about the Commandments?

4. What are the Commandments really about?

5. What does the Heavenly Father want most of all?

6. What is the next greatest Commandment?

7. If we want to be good, what must we do?

8. How can we divide the Ten Commandments into these Two Great Commandments?

Name:_____

Know, Love, and Serve God

What are some ways you can come to know, love, and serve God?

Know:

Love:

Serve:

Name:_____

Prayer

Answer the following questions in complete sentences.

1. What is prayer?

2. How often should we pray?

3. If we pray, what Commandment do we follow?

4. What are some reasons that people have for not praying?

5. Does God think our prayers are important?

6. Why does God want us to pray?

7. Does God always hear your prayers?

8. Does God always answer your prayers?

9. Does God always answer your prayers the way you expect him to?

Name:_____

God's Name

Answer the following questions in complete sentences.

1. Do you remember what God said his name was? He told Moses his name from the burning bush.

2. What does the way we talk about people tell others?

3. Why should we take care in talking about God?

4. What is the Second Commandment?

5. What does "in vain" mean?

6. How did the Jewish people respect God's name?

7. What did Jesus teach us to call God?

8. What is a special way that we can use God's name?

9. What prayers do you know that use God's name?

10. What other sins misuse God's name?

Name:_____

The Lord's Day

Answer the following questions in complete sentences.

1. What is the Third Commandment?

2. When do Israelites honor the Lord's Day?

3. When do Christians honor the Lord's Day?

4. Why do we honor Sunday as the Lord's Day?

5. What must we participate in on Sunday?

6. What can you do to make Sunday a holy and special day?

7. What can be left until the next day?

8. What are the Holy Days of Obligation?

Name:_____

God Loves You This Much!

God wants you to love yourself.

Name:_____

Honoring

Answer the following questions in complete sentences.

1. What is the Fourth Commandment?

2. What does this mean?

3. How do your parents love you?

4. What are some ways that you can love your parents?

5. How can you respect your parents?

6. How can you obey your parents?

7. Whom else should you honor?

Name:_____

Love Life!

Answer the following questions in complete sentences.

1. What is the Fifth Commandment?

2. How can you care for your body?

3. What kind of things can hurt your body?

4. How can you respect the bodies of other people?

5. What kinds of things hurt the bodies of other people?

6. How can you care for your soul?

Loving Others

Using a separate sheet of paper, describe what you would do in each of these situations and tell which Commandment helped you make your decision.

1. Your mother has told you to come home right after school, but since she will not be there, she would not know if you stopped at a friend's house first.

2. In your class there is a person that everyone makes fun of.

3. Sometimes your brother makes you so angry that you feel like hitting him.

4. Your mother asks you to help with the dishes even though it is not your turn to help.

5. Your babysitter tells you to go to bed, but you feel like staying up for a while longer.

6. Your friend is angry at you and does not want to be friends anymore.

7. Someone who has made you angry comes up to talk to you at school. You feel like ignoring him and walking away.

8. You are having your favorite dessert. You want to have a second helping, but you know you will feel sick if you have it.

Name:_____

Commandments 6 & 9

Answer the following questions in complete sentences.

1. What is the Sixth Commandment?

2. What is the Ninth Commandment?

3. What do these Commandments protect?

4. How do these Commandments have a message for you?

5. Families should model the Holy Family. What can you learn from the Holy Family?

Commandments 7 & 10

Answer the following questions in complete sentences.

1. What is the Seventh Commandment?

2. What is the Tenth Commandment?

3. What are some examples of stealing?

4. Why is this wrong if everything belongs to God?

5. Why is damaging other people's property wrong?

6. What does "covet" mean?

7. In order to be forgiven, must one try to make "restitution" (repair the damage)?

Name:_____

Commandment 8

Answer the following questions in complete sentences.

1. What is the Eighth Commandment?

2. Who is the "Father of Lies?" Why?

3. What is truth?

4. What must we do to keep the Eighth Commandment?

5. What might be some reasons why some people choose to lie?

6. What is exaggeration and flattery?

7. Why is gossiping bad?

Name:_____

Do's and Don'ts

Answer the following questions in complete sentences.

1. How can you be really happy in this life and in the next?

2. By keeping the Commandments, whose love do you reveal?

3. How does keeping the Commandments fulfill the laws of loving God and neighbor?

4. If you kept these Commandments, would you be a better person?

5. Why did God give us these Commandments?

6. How can you thank God for the Commandments?

Jesus

Jesus is both God and man. He is the Son of God from all eternity, and in time he became man through the power of the Holy Spirit in the womb of his mother, Mary. He has a body and soul as we do, yet he remains God. Jesus is one Divine Person, truly God and truly man. This is a mystery called the Incarnation, that God became man while remaining God.

Answer the following questions in complete sentences.

1. How many persons are there in Jesus?

2. How many natures does Jesus have?

3. What is a nature?

4. What are Jesus' two natures?

5. What is a mystery?

6. Is the mystery of the Incarnation contrary to our reason or beyond our reason?

7. Who is Jesus? Is he God?

Jesus Christ, True God and True Man

Answer the following questions in complete sentences.

1. Is Jesus Christ true God and true man?

2. How was the Son of God made man?

3. Did the Son of God cease being God when he became man?

4. Are there two natures in Jesus Christ?

5. With the two natures in Jesus Christ, are there also two persons?

6. What is a miracle?

7. What are some miracles that Jesus performed that show that he is God?

Name:_____

Jesus' Miracles

Jesus did miracles to show that he was not only sent from God, but that he is God!

List some of Jesus' miracles.

Name:_____

Jesus: The Only Way to Heaven

Answer the following questions in complete sentences.

1. How is Jesus like a best friend but only better?

2. Do you have to follow Jesus to get to heaven?

3. How can you grow closer to and follow your friend Jesus?

Write a prayer asking your friend Jesus to help you get to heaven.

Name:_____

God Saves Us

Answer the following questions in complete sentences.

1. Did God know that Adam and Eve would sin?

2. Why did God create them then?

3. What will happen at the end of the world?

4. Did the sin of Adam bring suffering into the world?

5. What was God's greatest gift of mercy?

6. Did we deserve a Redeemer?

7. How were we honored by God becoming man? What example can we use?

8. Was it easy for Jesus to redeem us?

Name:_____

Jesus Paid the Price of Our Sins

Circle the best answer.

1. In Jesus, God became:
   a. man
   b. our Savior
   c. the Messiah
   d. all of the above

2. Jesus as man:
   a. suffered and died
   b. could not die
   c. could not suffer
   d. could not suffer or die

3. Jesus was betrayed like this Old Testament figure:
   a. David
   b. Abraham
   c. Noah
   d. Joseph

4. Jesus suffered by
   a. sweating blood
   b. being scourged
   c. being crucified
   d. all of the above

5. The suffering and death of Jesus:
   a. were not painful
   b. opened the gates of heaven
   c. a and b
   d. neither a nor b

6. Jesus' sacrifice was the new:
   a. Passover
   b. wandering in the desert
   c. exile
   d. flood

7. Jesus himself was the:
   a. bitter herbs
   b. quail
   c. thunder
   d. paschal lamb

8. Jesus died on the Cross to:
   a. save us from sin
   b. give us his life
   c. open heaven for us
   d. all of the above

9. Jesus descended into hell to:
   a. fight the devil
   b. judge the dead
   c. lift the faithfully departed up to heaven
   d. suffer

Name:_____

The Resurrection

Answer the following questions in complete sentences.

1. What did Jesus mean when he said, "Destroy this temple, and in three days I will raise it up"?

2. How is Jesus' Body like a temple?

Name:_____

The Ascension

Answer the following questions in complete sentences.

1. Before Jesus returned to his Father,
   what did Jesus do and why?

2. What did his friends think when they
   first saw Jesus?

3. How did Jesus prove he
   had risen?

4. Forty days after his Resurrection, what did Jesus do?

Name:_____

Sacrifices

Things to think about.

Abel, Noah, Abraham, Isaac, Jacob and many others offered sacrifices to God to adore and thank him for his many gifts and also to ask for his blessings.

When they sinned, they offered up atonement (make up for) sacrifices to God.

They would take their best animals or crops—things that would have been good to eat or could have been sold for a lot of money—and they offered them up. By burning them, they offered what was dear to them and gave them back to God completely.

The Perfect Sacrifice

Things to think about.

Since Adam had sinned, and all of mankind in him, sacrifice which involved blood was needed to atone for sin. The sprinkling of blood was the most important part of the sacrifice. The lamb or other animal victim had to be the best of the flock. The priest would lay his hands on the animal's head to transfer the man's sins onto it.

Jesus' Blood was shed for us on the Cross as an atonement sacrifice for our sins. Jesus was called the spotless lamb because he is not only sinless and perfect, but he is also God. Jesus really took our sins upon himself and died for our sakes.

Name:_____

The Sacrifice of the Mass

This is my Body.
This is the chalice of my Blood,
the Blood of the new and eternal covenant,
which will be poured out for you and for many
for the forgivness of sins.
Do this in memory of me.

Name:_____

The Mass

Answer the following questions in complete sentences.

1. What is the Holy Mass?

2. What is a sacrifice?

3. Is the Sacrifice of the Mass the same as the Sacrifice of the Cross?

4. What is the difference between the Sacrifice of the Cross and the Sacrifice of the Mass?

5. Are we obliged to hear Mass? When?

6. What are the two parts of the Mass?

Name:_____

Bread of Life

Fill in the blanks with the help of your student text.

You remember when the children of _____ were in the

_____ and did not have enough food. They complained to

_____ that it was impossible for them to continue their pilgrim

_____ to the _____ _____ because they

were hungry and too weak. Then _____ heard their prayers and had

pity on them. In his great _____ he would send them food. "I

will rain down _____ from _____ for you," he said

to Moses.

The next morning they found the ground covered with a delicate and

flaky white substance with a wonderfully sweet _____, like wafers

made with _____.

In order to help you and give you strength for your _____ on

this earth on your way to _____ (our Promised Land), you too can

have _____ from _____. This bread that you can receive

is much, much better than _____ because if you eat it, you will have

_____ life! You receive this _____

_____ every time you go to _____ _____!

But how can bread be "living" or alive? This bread is not really bread!

It looks and tastes like bread, but it is really _____ hidden under the

appearance of bread.

Jesus said, "I am the _____ _____, which comes

down from heaven. If anyone eats of this _____, he will live

_____. And the bread which I give for the life of the world is my

_____."

Name:_____

Jesus Is With Us Too!

Things to think about.

During the Liturgy of the Eucharist, the Mass follows closely what Jesus himself did at the Last Supper. The priest does the actions and says the words of Jesus.

At the exact moment when the priest says, "This is my Body," the bread is no longer bread because it has been completely changed into the Body, Blood, Soul, and Divinity of Christ. When he says, "This is the chalice of my Blood," the wine is no longer wine because it too has been completely changed into Jesus' Body, Blood, Soul, and Divinity.

Jesus is now really and truly present, Body, Blood, Soul, and Divinity, in the Eucharist. Each particle of every consecrated Host and each drop of consecrated wine is truly Jesus whole and entire. Jesus gives himself completely to us in Holy Communion.

Name:_____

A Holy Meal

Things to think about.

The Eucharist is a holy meal where Christ gives himself to us as food, the Living Bread from heaven. We share this Paschal meal (the Passover) of Jesus' life, death, and Resurrection. We share in Jesus' triumph over sin and death, and he gives us strength to break away from sin. We are all united in this Communion with God and with each other.

Bread from Heaven

Draw lines connecting the first part of each sentence with the correct ending.

You can eat Living Bread...

...the bread changes into the Body, Blood, Soul, and Divinity of Christ.

When the priest says, "This is my Body"...

...every time you go to Communion.

Even the tiniest piece of the Host...

...the wine changes into the Body, Blood, Soul, and Divinity of Christ.

Jesus is in the Eucharist...

...for you to come and visit him.

When the priest says, "This is the chalice of my Blood"...

...is truly Jesus: Body, Blood, Soul, and Divinity.

Jesus waits in the tabernacle...

...because he wants you to receive him often.

What are the steps to receiving Jesus worthily in Holy Communion?

1.

2.

3.

Name:_____

Effects of Original Sin

Answer the following questions in complete sentences.

1. What did God warn would happen to Adam and Eve if they turned away from him?

2. What happened when they disobeyed God?

3. Who else suffers from the disobedience of Adam and Eve?

4. How was grace won back for us?

5. How do we receive this grace?

6. After we have been baptized, do we still have the effects of Original Sin in us?

Name:_____

Sin

Answer the following questions in complete sentences.

1. What is your conscience?

2. What helps you to know right from wrong?

3. Why do you sometimes not listen to your conscience?

4. Should your reason and conscience rule your actions?

5. Do our desires sometimes rule our actions?

6. When do we sin?

7. Who committed the first sin?

8. What is this sin called?

9. What are all other sins called?

10. What does sin do to us on our way to heaven?

Name: _____

Actual Sin, Mortal Sin, & Venial Sin

ACTUAL SIN: when we sin with our thoughts, words, actions, or omissions.

VENIAL SIN: weakens the soul.	MORTAL SIN: kills the life of grace in the soul.
Breaks God's laws in a less serious way	Breaks God's laws in a serious way
We do not know the full seriousness of our action	We must know that it is serious
We do not fully choose to break a serious law	We choose freely to break a serious law
We did not think about it	We thought about it
We did not fully intend to do it	We did it on purpose
Venial sins slow down our way to heaven	If we die in mortal sin, we risk going to hell forever

O my God, I am heartily sorry for having offended thee.
I detest all my sins because of thy just punishments,
but most of all because they offend thee, my God,
who art all good and deserving of all my love.
I firmly resolve, with the help of thy grace,
to confess my sins, to do penance,
and to amend my life. Amen.

Name:_____

Mistakes Along the Way

Circle the best answer.

1. The judgment you make about how you ought to act or not act is called your
   a. context
   b. conscience
   c. constant

2. Choosing to do something that we know is against God's laws is
   a. an accident
   b. a temptation
   c. a sin

3. The type of sin that kills the life of grace in the soul is
   a. Original Sin
   b. mortal sin
   c. venial sin

4. The kind of sin that offends God in a smaller way than mortal sin is
   a. Original Sin
   b. mortal sin
   c. venial sin

5. Thinking something unkind about another is a sin of
   a. thought
   b. word
   c. action
   d. omission

6. Not doing the dishes when we are told to is a sin of
   a. thought
   b. word
   c. action
   d. omission

7. Telling a lie is a sin of
   a. thought
   b. word
   c. action
   d. omission

8. Cheating on a test is a sin of
   a. thought
   b. word
   c. action
   d. omission

Name:_____

Word Find

Find the following words in the puzzle below. Note that the words could be diagonal, vertical, or horizontal!

Absolution	Examination	Money	Sacrament
Actual	Flattery	Mortal	Sin
Blasphemy	Grace	Patience	Sorrow
Confession	Hate	Penance	Venial
Conscience	Idols	Reconciliation	

```
S  A  C  R  A  M  E  N  T  P  O  I  X  C  B  B
G  R  A  C  E  L  R  A  Q  E  R  X  O  O  L  N
F  L  A  T  T  E  R  Y  T  N  A  N  S  N  A  A
T  P  R  M  T  A  E  T  W  A  S  U  O  F  S  C
S  G  X  T  A  D  N  M  R  N  W  K  R  E  P  T
M  L  A  H  G  R  D  O  I  C  Z  N  R  S  H  U
C  L  B  A  X  N  C  R  E  E  M  R  O  S  E  A
F  K  R  T  P  A  N  T  N  W  W  R  W  I  M  L
M  O  N  E  Y  C  M  A  S  M  O  T  G  O  Y  A
X  O  N  J  E  G  L  L  P  A  T  I  E  N  C  E
E  X  A  M  I  N  A  T  I  O  N  S  V  C  M  L
R  E  C  O  N  C  I  L  I  A  T  I  O  N  O  I
A  B  S  O  L  U  T  I  O  N  T  N  F  T  J  D
V  E  N  I  A  L  Z  G  O  B  C  I  U  P  B  O
H  P  V  Y  U  N  V  Y  F  L  X  A  O  H  T  L
C  O  N  S  C  I  E  N  C  E  L  B  G  N  N  S
```

Name:_____

The Prodigal Son

Answer the following questions in complete sentences.

1. Why did the younger son leave his father?

2. What did he do with his father's gift of money?

3. How did he support himself during the famine?

4. Why did he return home?

5. How was he received by his father?

Name:_____

God Forgives

Answer the following questions in complete sentences.

1. Is God always willing to forgive us?

2. Is there a sin too big for Jesus to forgive?

3. What gift did Jesus give us to have our sins forgiven?

4. What are some other names for this gift?

5. Explain the three steps to prepare for Confession.

Examination of conscience:

Sorrow for sins:

Intention to avoid sins:

Name:_____

Steps to a Good Confession

Check off each step as you complete it.

☐   1. Examination of conscience

       Think about the Ten Commandments listed in your student text and think about whether you have broken any of them.

☐   2. Tell Jesus you are sorry for the sins that you have committed. Ask for his help to make you truly sorry and for his grace so you will not commit those sins again.

☐   3. Make up your mind to avoid those sins in the future.

☐   4. Go into the confessional. Tell the priest your sins. Listen for any words of advice from the priest about how you can become better. Also, listen for your penance. Say an Act of Contrition:

O my God, I am heartily sorry for having offended thee.
I detest all my sins because of thy just punishments,
but most of all because they offend thee, my God,
who art all good and deserving of all my love.
I firmly resolve, with the help of thy grace,
to confess my sins, to do penance,
and to amend my life. Amen.

☐   5. Do the penance the priest has assigned to you.

Name:_____

The Trinity

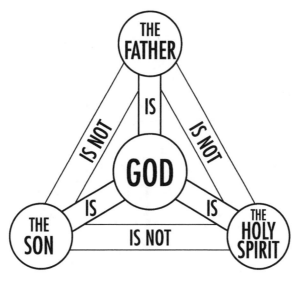

Answer the following questions in complete sentences.

1. How many Persons are there in God?

2. What do we call this mystery?

3. Who is the First Person of the Blessed Trinity? For what is he known?

4. Who is the Second Person of the Blessed Trinity? For what is he known?

5. Who is the Third Person of the Blessed Trinity? For what is he known?

6. Are all these Persons equal?

Name:_____

Holy Spirit

Answer the following questions in complete sentences.

1. Why can we say that when God gives us something out of love, it is the work of the Holy Spirit?

2. When did you receive the Holy Spirit for the first time?

3. Does the Holy Spirit live in you?

4. When will you become an even stronger follower of Jesus in the Holy Spirit?

Name:_____

The Holy Spirit

True or false questions.

1. _____ There are three Gods: the Father, the Son, and the Holy Spirit.

2. _____ God the Son is Jesus.

3. _____ The Holy Spirit is the Second Person of the Blessed Trinity.

4. _____ The Holy Spirit came down in the form of a dove at Jesus' Baptism.

5. _____ The Holy Spirit is the love between the Father and the Son.

6. _____ We worship a different God than the one Abraham worshipped.

7. _____ All three Persons of the Holy Trinity are one and the same God.

8. _____ The first time the Holy Spirit came into your soul was at your Baptism.

9. _____ Confirmation is the Sacrament where the Holy Spirit comes and makes us even stronger followers of Jesus.

10. _____ The Holy Spirit filled the apostles and the mother of Jesus with his strength on Pentecost.

Name:_____

The Spirit of Truth

Unscramble these words to find out the answers.

1. What are three names for the Holy Spirit?

CLTEEAARP

UOCNLOERS

TTTFSOPIIRRUH

2. Jesus promised not to leave his apostles as what?

POSRNAH

3. Where did Mary and the apostles pray?

MREJSLEAU

4. How did the Holy Spirit appear?

FRGTUONEIFSEO

5. What is the feast called when we celebrate the coming of the Holy Spirit?

EEPCTTNOS

6. Why is the day special for us?

YTHRCCHHURFOBIADEHT

Name:_____

The People of God

Answer the following questions in complete sentences.

1. What is another name for the People of God?

2. What does it mean to be part of a community?

3. What does the Church offer us?

4. What is the Mystical Body of Christ?

5. Who gives life to the Mystical Body?

6. Who is included in the Mystical Body of Christ?

7. Do we all share the same work and talents in this Mystical Body?

God's Chosen People

Give examples of how you can be:

A priestly people

A kingly people

A prophetic people

Name:_____

The Pope

You are Peter, and on this rock I will build my Church, and the gates of Hades shall not prevail against it. I will give you the keys of the kingdom of heaven, and whatever you bind on earth shall be bound in heaven, and whatever you loose on earth shall be loosed in heaven.

Answer the following questions in complete sentences.

1. What is infallibility?

2. Who has the gift of infallibility (alone or with other people)?

3. On what matters does infallible teaching apply?

4. Who is the Pope?

The Church of Christ

What would you tell each of the boys and girls in the situations below? Use your student text if you need help.

1. Steve tells his Lutheran friend, Bill, that he is not Jesus' follower because he is not in the Catholic Church.

2. Katie says that it does not make any difference which church one belongs to.

3. Tony says that unless the words of the Pope and the bishops are guarded by infallibility, we do not have to listen to them or obey them.

4. Margaret says that we cannot be sure that we are receiving Christ's teaching two thousand years after he ascended into heaven.

5. Greg would like to know who the first Pope was and who the Pope is now.

6. Nancy says that it is not anyone else's business what she does. Her sins only hurt herself.

Name:_____

Grace

Answer the following questions in complete sentences.

1. What nine things should we know about grace?

    a.

    b.

    c.

    d.

    e.

    f.

    g.

    h.

    i.

2. How did mankind lose grace?

3. How was it won back for us?

Name:_____

Channels of Grace

Draw lines matching the Sacrament on the left with the proper effects from the column on the right.

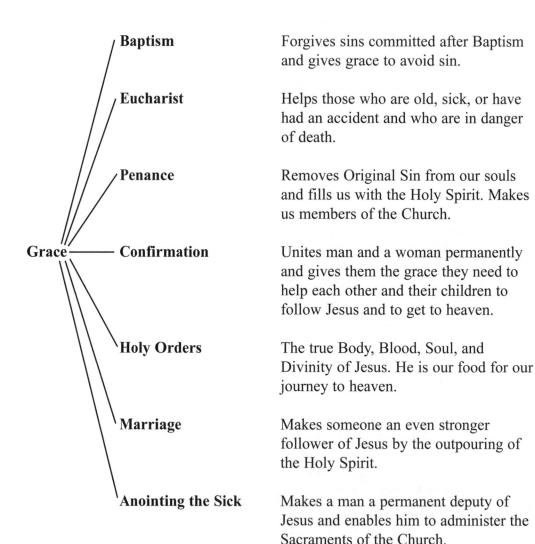

Baptism

Forgives sins committed after Baptism and gives grace to avoid sin.

Eucharist

Helps those who are old, sick, or have had an accident and who are in danger of death.

Penance

Removes Original Sin from our souls and fills us with the Holy Spirit. Makes us members of the Church.

Grace ——— Confirmation

Unites man and a woman permanently and gives them the grace they need to help each other and their children to follow Jesus and to get to heaven.

Holy Orders

The true Body, Blood, Soul, and Divinity of Jesus. He is our food for our journey to heaven.

Marriage

Makes someone an even stronger follower of Jesus by the outpouring of the Holy Spirit.

Anointing the Sick

Makes a man a permanent deputy of Jesus and enables him to administer the Sacraments of the Church.

Name:_____

Baptism

Answer the following questions in complete sentences.

1. What did you become at your Baptism?

2. What journey did your Baptism start you on?

3. What was removed from your soul at Baptism?

4. Whom did you receive at Baptism?

5. Write a little prayer thanking God for your Baptism.

Name:_____

Penance

Answer the following questions in complete sentences.

1. Why do we need to go to Confession?

2. What does this Sacrament do for us?

3. Do our sins hurt just ourselves?

4. What does the Sacrament of Penance give us and why?

5. Write a short prayer asking Jesus to help you keep a healthy soul and to help you to make a good Confession so you can go to heaven.

Name:_____

Eucharist

Answer the following questions in complete sentences.

1. Why is the Eucharist the center of Catholic life?

2. What is the Eucharist food for?

3. How is Jesus present in the Eucharist?

4. Do we receive grace when we receive Holy Communion?

5. Write a little prayer thanking Jesus for the Eucharist.

Name:_____

Confirmation

Answer the following questions in complete sentences.

1. What does the Sacrament of Confirmation do for you?

2. How are you marked in the Sacrament of Confirmation?

3. What will you be responsible for once you are confirmed?

4. Write a prayer asking God to prepare you for the Sacrament of Confirmation.

Matrimony

Answer the following questions in complete sentences.

1. What do married people do for each other and why?

2. How must married people care for their children?

3. Write a short prayer asking for the gift to be a good husband or wife.

Name:_____

Holy Orders

Answer the following questions in complete sentences.

1. Who can be a priest?

2. What do priests do?

3. Who works through the priest?

4. Write a short prayer asking Jesus to give the Church many good priests.

Name:_____

Anointing of the Sick

Answer the following questions.

1. What can being sick do to you?

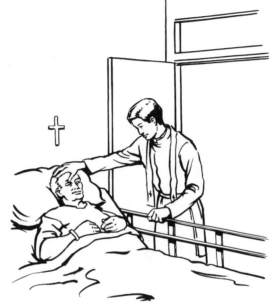

2. For whom is this Sacrament?

3. What happens in this Sacrament?

4. What does this Sacrament do?

5. Write a short prayer asking Jesus for the grace to be able to receive this Sacrament if you become very sick or old.

This page intentionally left blank.

Name:_____

Immaculate Mary

True or false questions.

1. _____ Mary was without sin, even Original Sin.

2. _____ Mary said yes to God throughout her whole life.

3. _____ Mary did not always do God's will.

4. _____ Mary taught Jesus.

5. _____ Mary did not know that Jesus was God.

6. _____ Mary became the mother of Jesus by the power of the Holy Spirit.

7. _____ Mary is a good model of faith and virtue for each one of us.

Name:_____

The Assumption

Circle the best answer.

1. Mary went to heaven:
   a. as a soul   b. with body and soul   c. after time in purgatory   d. none

2. Mary was taken to heaven:
   a. by the apostles   b. at the end of her earthly life   c. by Jesus   d. b and c

3. In heaven, Mary is:
   a. Queen of all creation   b. Mother of the Church   c. Praying for us   d. a, b, and c

4. Jesus loves Mary so much that he wants her to share in:
   a. his glories and honors   b. the Trinity   c. his humanity   d. none

Faith and Life Series • Grade 4 • Chapter 29 • Lesson 2

Name:_____

Our Mother, Mary

Use your student text to solve this crossword puzzle.

Across

2. The name of our heavenly mother.
4. The taking up of Mary's body and soul into heaven.
5. When we pray to Mary, she _____ Jesus to help us.
6. Mary is watching over us from _____.
8. You are Mary's own _____.

Down

1. When we talk to Mary and ask for her prayers, we _____ to her.
2. Mary is our heavenly _____.
3. Mary always leads us to _____.
7. Mary is sometimes called the second _____.

Mary Leads to Jesus

Answer the following questions in complete sentences.

1. What should we do to have Mary lead us to Jesus?

2. When did God show us that Mary's prayers are answered?

3. What can you ask Mary to pray for?

4. What advice did Mary give us?

Name:_____

Heaven, Our Home

Write a letter to God asking him to take you home when your time on earth is done.

Dear God,

Name:_____

Judgment

Answer the following questions in complete sentences.

1. When will the Particular Judgment occur?

2. On what will we be judged?

3. When will the General Judgment occur?

4. What will happen during the General Judgment?

5. Will people go to purgatory at the General Judgment? Where will they go?

Name:_____

We Reach Our Goal

Write a description of what you think it will be like to meet Jesus when you die.

Draw lines to connect the words in the left column with the matching words in the right column.

General Judgment   when Jesus will return to earth again

heaven   never-ending separation from God

thoughts, words, actions,   suffering after death which purifies souls
and omissions   and helps them to make up for their sins
                                           committed while they were alive

end of the world   the raising of all bodies from the dead and
                                           the reuniting of them with their souls at
                                           the end of the world

Particular Judgment   the judgment of the entire human race at
                                           the end of the world

hell   eternal life and happiness with God

purgatory   the things that Jesus will judge us on

resurrection of the body   the individual judgment of each person by
                                           Jesus

Reaching Our Goal

Answer the following questions in complete sentences.

1. When you die, what will happen to you?

2. On what will you be judged?

3. What happens if you need to be purified before entering heaven?

4. What is heaven like?

5. Who will never get to heaven? Where do they go?

6. Do we deserve punishment? How can we still have hope?